C000154715

Improving
Punctuation

for ages 7-8

A & C Black • London

Introduction

Following the success of the Improving Comprehension, Improving Writing and Improving Spelling series, *Improving Punctuation* contains a range of activities to provide practice in the difficult skills of punctuation. The targets have been carefully selected to be appropriate to the age group and to progress in their level of difficulty. The accompanying worksheets are differentiated at three levels and are designed to be used by individuals or small groups. **Notes for teachers** at the foot of each worksheet provide guidance on how to get the most from the targets and how to approach the questions on the sheet.

How to use the book and CD-ROM together

The National Curriculum at Key Stage 1 states that pupils should be taught:
a. how punctuation helps a reader understand what is written;
b. the connections between punctuation and sentence structure, intonation and emphasis;
c. to use capital letters, full stops, question marks and to begin to use commas.

At Key Stage 2, 'pupils should be taught to use punctuation marks correctly in their writing, including full stops, question and exclamation marks, commas, inverted commas, and apostrophes to mark possession and omission.'

The activities presented within this book provide opportunities for revising all of the punctuation aspects at Key Stage 1 and for introducing some of the skills required at Key Stage 2 of the National Curriculum. The book has fifteen targets, which can be projected onto a whiteboard for whole class use from the CD-ROM, or photocopied/printed for display. Sharing the worksheet activities either on screen or paper provides lots of opportunities for speaking and listening, for decoding words through a phonic approach, for reading and re-reading for meaning and for satisfaction and enjoyment in shared success.

For each target there are three punctuation worksheets at different ability levels to enable teachers to differentiate across the ability range. An animal picture at the top of the sheet indicates the level of the worksheet. The cat exercises are at the simplest level; the dog exercises are at the next level; the rabbit exercises are at the most advanced level. You may decide to give some pupils the cat worksheet and then decide, on the basis of their success, to ask them to complete the dog worksheet. A similar approach could be taken with the dog and rabbit sheets.

After reading the target with the pupils, the teacher should discuss the tasks ensuring that the children understand clearly how to complete the worksheet. Remind them to answer the questions using full sentences and correct punctuation.

National Curriculum levels

The worksheets are aimed at the following ability levels:

Cat worksheets are for pupils working towards Level 2.
Dog worksheets are for pupils working at Level 2.
Rabbit worksheets are for pupils who are working confidently at Level 2 and are progressing towards Level 3.

To achieve the punctuation aspect of writing at Level 1, pupils 'begin to show awareness of how full stops are used'. At Level 2: 'Ideas are developed in a sequence of sentences, sometimes demarcated by capital letters and full stops.' At Level 3: 'Punctuation to mark sentences – full stops, capital letters and question marks – is used accurately.' For Level 4: 'Full stops, capital letters and question marks are used correctly, and pupils are beginning to use punctuation within the sentence.'

Note that what the National Curriculum requires to be taught goes significantly beyond what is required to achieve the stated levels. The experiences pupils of all abilities will gain through working on the activities in this book will ensure that they cover the demands of the National Curriculum and will serve them in good stead in applying their skills to their everyday writing. This will help them to achieve the punctuation aspects of their appropriate level.

Contents

Alphabet sheet

aA   bB   cC   dD

eE   fF   gG   hH

iI   jJ   kK   lL

mM   nN   oO   pP

qQ   rR   sS   tT

uU   vV   wW   xX

yY   zZ

Notes for teachers

Throughout Key Stage 2 some pupils find confusion between capital and lower case letters. This alphabet sheet provides opportunities for discussing and comparing the letters. You may like to pay particular attention to letter j in both its forms as many children mix these when writing.

Remember to use a capital letter at the start and a full stop at the end of each sentence.

Name: Date:

Target 1

Remember to use a capital letter at the start and a full stop at the end of each sentence.

The sentences below should each have a capital letter at the start and a full stop at the end. Write the sentences correctly.

yesterday was a lovely day

today it is raining

Write your own sentence about something that happened yesterday. Do not forget to use a capital letter at the start and a full stop at the end.

_____

_____

Write your own sentence about something that happened today. Do not forget to use a capital letter at the start and a full stop at the end.

_____

_____

Notes for teachers

Help the children to read the target. Remind them of the capital letters by discussing the alphabet sheet with them. Read through the information and instructions on this worksheet, supporting the children in using their phonic skills to decode the words. Encourage the pupils to read the sentences out loud so that they can 'hear' where each one ends. Help them to think of ideas for their own sentences: they could write about quite ordinary events such as eating a meal, going out somewhere, getting ready for school, etc. You may like to extend the activity by asking the children to write about something that may happen tomorrow.

Andrew Brodie: Improving Punctuation for Ages 7–8 © A&C Black, Bloomsbury Publishing 2012

Name: _____ Date: _____

Target 1

Remember to use a capital letter at the start and a full stop at the end of each sentence.

The sentences below should each have a capital letter at the start and a full stop at the end. Write the sentences correctly.

we are going swimming at the weekend

_____

last weekend we went to the seaside

_____

Write your own sentence about something that you hope to do in the next few days. Do not forget to use a capital letter at the start and a full stop at the end.

_____

_____

Write your own sentence about something that you did last weekend. Do not forget to use a capital letter at the start and a full stop at the end.

_____

_____

Notes for teachers
Help the children to read the target. Remind them of the capital letters by discussing the alphabet sheet with them. Read through the information and instructions on this worksheet, supporting the children in using their phonic skills to decode the words. Encourage the pupils to read the sentences out loud so that they can 'hear' where each one ends. Point out that the first sentence is about something that is going to happen in the future and the second sentence is about something that happened in the past. Help them to think of ideas for their own sentences: they could write about quite ordinary events such as going shopping, visiting relatives, watching a particular television show, etc. You may like to extend the activity by asking the children to write more than one sentence for each of the two tasks.

Target 1

Remember to use a capital letter at the start and a full stop at the end of each sentence.

Each piece of writing below needs to be written as two sentences. Can you decide how to punctuate them correctly?

last weekend we went shopping i was very bored

_____

_____

the journey home from the shops took over an hour it was quite late when we got in

_____

_____

Write your own sentences about something that you hope to do in the next few days. Do not forget to use a capital letter at the start and a full stop at the end of each sentence.

_____

_____

_____

_____

_____

Notes for teachers
Ask the children to read through the information and instructions on this worksheet. Encourage the pupils to read the pieces of writing out loud so that they can 'hear' where each sentence ends. Help them to think of ideas for their own sentences: they could write about quite ordinary events such as going shopping, visiting relatives, watching a particular television show, etc.

Remember to use a capital letter at the start of each sentence and at the start of each person's name.

Remember to use a capital letter at the start of each sentence and at the start of each person's name.

Write these sentences correctly. Do not forget the full stops.

will and jasmin went swimming yesterday

_____

rob is going to play with tom after school today

_____

Write your own sentence about something that you have done with a friend. Remember to use a capital letter at the start and a full stop at the end. Do not forget to use a capital letter for the start of any names.

_____

_____

Think about one of your friends. What is your friend good at? Write a sentence about this.

_____

_____

Notes for teachers

Help the children to read the target. Remind them of the capital letters by discussing the alphabet sheet with them – draw their attention to the capital and lower case versions of letter j, as many pupils make errors with this. Read through the information and instructions on this worksheet, supporting the children in using their phonic skills to decode the words. Encourage the pupils to read the sentences out loud so that they can 'hear' where each one ends. Help them to think of ideas for their own sentences.

Target 2

Remember to use a capital letter at the start of each sentence and at the start of each person's name.

Write these sentences correctly. Do not forget the full stops.

tariq and esme were the first people to finish the maths

_____

_____

oliver and katie are both really good at football

_____

_____

Write your own sentence about two people in your class. You must not write anything unkind about them. Do not forget to use a capital letter for the start of any names. Remember to use a capital letter at the start and a full stop at the end.

_____

_____

Write about two people who are good at something.

_____

_____

Notes for teachers
Help the children to read the target. Remind them of the capital letters by discussing the alphabet sheet with them. Read through the information and instructions on this worksheet, supporting the children in using their phonic skills to decode the words. Encourage the pupils to read the sentences out loud so that they can 'hear' where each one ends. Help them to think of ideas for their own sentences, ensuring that they don't write anything inappropriate.

Target 2

Remember to use a capital letter at the start of each sentence and at the start of each person's name.

Each piece of writing below needs to be written as two sentences. Can you decide how to punctuate them correctly?

george and lily worked hard on their homework george wrote more than a page

_____

_____

the teacher asked rebecca and alison to tidy the classroom they stayed in at breaktime to do it

_____

_____

Write your own sentences about two people you know. Do not forget to use a capital letter at the start and a full stop at the end of each sentence.

_____

_____

_____

_____

_____

Notes for teachers
Ask the children to read through the information and instructions on this worksheet. Encourage the pupils to read the pieces of writing out loud so that they can 'hear' where each sentence ends. Help them to think of ideas for their own sentences, ensuring that they do not write anything inappropriate, which could be upsetting for the subjects.

Remember to use a capital letter at the start of each sentence and for the start of each day of the week.

Remember to use a capital letter at the start of each sentence and for the start of each day of the week.

Write these sentences correctly. Do not forget the full stops.

saturday and sunday are both at the weekend

_____

the first day of the school week is monday

_____

_____

What day was it the day before yesterday? Write about something that happened that day. Remember to use a capital letter at the start and a full stop at the end. Do not forget to use a capital letter for the start of any days of the week.

_____

_____

Write about something you might do next Saturday.

_____

_____

Notes for teachers
Help the children to read the target. Read through the information and instructions on this worksheet, supporting the children in using their phonic skills to decode the words. Encourage the pupils to read the sentences out loud so that they can 'hear' where each one ends. Help them to think of ideas for their own sentences.

Target 3

Remember to use a capital letter at the start of each sentence and for the start of each day of the week.

Write these sentences correctly. Do not forget the full stops.

the day before friday is thursday

_____

my last birthday was on a wednesday

_____

What is your favourite day of the week? Write a sentence about it. Remember to use a capital letter at the start and a full stop at the end. Do not forget to use a capital letter for the start of any days of the week.

_____

_____

_____

What is your least favourite day of the week?

_____

_____

_____

Notes for teachers
Help the children to read the target. Read through the information and instructions on this worksheet, supporting the children in using their phonic skills to decode the words. Encourage the pupils to read the sentences out loud so that they can 'hear' where each one ends. Help them to think of ideas for their own sentences.

Target 3

Remember to use a capital letter at the start of each sentence and for the start of each day of the week.

Each piece of writing below needs to be written as two sentences. Can you decide how to punctuate them correctly?

on tuesday we visited a castle we had to write about it on wednesday

_____

_____

_____

the busiest day was thursday we had to do maths and science

_____

_____

Write your own sentences about things you have done this week. What have you done each day so far?

_____

_____

_____

_____

_____

Notes for teachers
Ask the children to read through the information and instructions on this worksheet. Encourage the pupils to read the sentences out loud so that they can 'hear' where each one ends. Help them to think of ideas for their own sentences.

Remember
to use a capital letter at the start of each sentence and for the start of each month of the year.

Target 4

Remember to use a capital letter at the start of each sentence and for the start of each month of the year.

Read the names of the months in the word bank.
Write the months in the correct order.

Word bank
March
October
December
January
April
June
February
May
August
November
July
September

_____

_____

_____

_____

_____

_____

_____

_____

_____

_____

_____

_____

What month was it last month? Write your answer in a sentence.

_____

_____

Notes for teachers
Help the children to read the target. They may need some help in composing their own sentence for the final task. Do they remember to write capital letters for the sentence start and for months and do they remember the full stop at the end of their sentence?

Target 4

Remember to use a capital letter at the start of each sentence and for the start of each month of the year.

Read the names of the months in the word bank.

Word bank

January   February   March   April   May   June   July   August
September   October   November   December

Answer each question carefully. Write each answer as a sentence.

What is the eighth month of the year?

_____

_____

Which month comes straight before October?

_____

_____

Which month comes straight after October?

_____

_____

Notes for teachers
Help the children to read the target. Do they remember to write capital letters for each sentence start and for months and do they remember the full stops at the ends of their sentences?

Target 4

> **Remember to use a capital letter at the start of each sentence and for the start of each month of the year.**

Read the names of the months in the word bank.

Word bank
January February March April May June July August
September October November December

Answer each question carefully. Write each answer as a sentence.

In which month is your birthday?

_____

_____

Describe what the weather might be like in January.

_____

_____

Describe what the weather might be like in July.

_____

_____

Notes for teachers
Help the children to read the target. Do they remember to write capital letters for each sentence start and for months and do they remember the full stops at the ends of their sentences? They may need some help in remembering the type of weather that might be found in January or July. Encourage them to consider how warm the weather may be in each month.

Remember to use question marks for questions.

Remember to use question marks for questions.

In the question bank there are some question sentences.

Question bank

How old are you?   When is your birthday?

Do you like football?   Do you like watching television?

Have you got a pet?   Do you live in a house?

Have you got any brothers or sisters?

Choose two sentences to ask a friend. Write out the sentences and write the answers as well.

Question _____

_____

Answer _____

_____

Question _____

_____

Answer _____

_____

Notes for teachers

Help the children to read the target. Read through the information and instructions on this worksheet, supporting the children in using their phonic skills to decode the words. When you are confident that the children understand the activity, help them to choose two questions, then to ask a friend the questions. Ensure that they use a question mark at the end of each question and a full stop at the end of each answer.

Name: _____ Date: _____

Target 5

Remember to use question marks for questions.

In the question bank there are some question sentences.

Question bank

What is your favourite food?   What is your favourite drink?
Which food do you like the least?
What is your favourite sport?   Where do you live?
Where did you last go on holiday?

Choose two sentences to ask a friend. Write out the sentences and write the answers as well.

Question _____

_____

Answer _____

_____

Question _____

_____

Answer _____

_____

Notes for teachers
Help the children to read the target. When you are confident that the children understand the activity, help them to choose two questions, then to ask a friend the questions. Ensure that they use a question mark at the end of each question and a full stop at the end of each answer.

Target 5

Remember to use question marks for questions.

In the question bank there are some question sentences but they are not punctuated.

Question bank

where do you live   do you have any pets

what is your favourite food   what is your favourite sport

which school subject do you like best   when is your birthday

what did you do at the weekend

Choose two sentences to ask a friend. Write out the sentences with correct punctuation. Write your friend's answers as well.

Question _____

_____

Answer _____

_____

Question _____

_____

Answer _____

_____

Notes for teachers

Help the children to read the target. When you are confident that the children understand the activity, help them to choose two questions, then to ask a friend the questions. Ensure that they use a question mark at the end of each question and a full stop at the end of each answer. Do they remember the capital letter for the start of each sentence?

Remember when to use question marks and when to use full stops.

Target 6

Remember when to use question marks and when to use full stops.

Sentence bank

How old are you?   I would like a new bike.

When is your birthday?   I am eight years old.

My birthday is in January.

What would you like for your birthday?

Read the sentences in the sentence bank.

Some of the sentences are questions.

Some of the sentences are answers to the

questions. Write the pairs of sentences that go together.

_____

_____

_____

_____

_____

_____

Notes for teachers

Help the children to read the target and to read the instructions: these are quite complicated and the children may need to read them several times. When you are confident that the children understand the activity, ask them to copy the sentences correctly. Can they match the questions and the answers? Do they remember to use question marks for the question sentences, full stops for the answer sentences, and capital letters for the starts of sentences and of the name of the month?

Target 6

Remember when to use question marks and when to use full stops.

Sentence bank

which is the biggest mammal in the world

what is the biggest fish in the world

what is the biggest bird in the world

the biggest fish is the whale shark

the biggest mammal is the blue whale

the biggest bird is the ostrich

Read the sentences in the sentence bank. Some of the sentences are questions. Some of the sentences are answers to the questions. Write the pairs of sentences that go together.

_____

_____

_____

_____

_____

_____

Notes for teachers

Help the children to read the target and to read the instructions: these are quite complicated and the children may need to read them several times. When you are confident that the children understand the activity, ask them to copy the sentences correctly. Can they match the questions and the answers? Do they remember to use question marks for the question sentences, full stops for the answer sentences, and capital letters for the starts of sentences? Ensure that they do not capitalize the initial letters of the animal names – these are nouns, not proper nouns.

Target 6

Remember when to use question marks and when to use full stops.

Sentence bank

which is the highest mountain in the world

what is the name of the longest river in the world

which is the biggest ocean in the world

the longest river is the nile

the biggest ocean is the pacific

the highest mountain is everest

Read the sentences in the sentence bank. Some of the sentences are questions. Some of the sentences are answers to the questions. Write the pairs of sentences that go together.

_____

_____

_____

_____

_____

_____

Notes for teachers

Help the children to read the target and to read the instructions: these are quite complicated and the children may need to read them several times. When you are confident that the children understand the activity, ask them to copy the sentences correctly. Can they match the questions and the answers? Do they remember to use question marks for the question sentences, full stops for the answer sentences, and capital letters for the starts of sentences and of the names?

Remember to use a capital letter at the start of each person's name. Remember to use question marks for questions.

Target 7

Remember to use a capital letter at the start of each person's name. Remember to use question marks for questions.

Sentence bank

Who played football yesterday?

Who went swimming yesterday?

What did Jasdeep do yesterday?

Yesterday Jasdeep visited her uncle.

Yesterday Liz went swimming.

Yesterday Tom played football.

Read the sentences in the sentence bank. Some of the sentences are questions. Some of the sentences are answers to the questions. Write the pairs of sentences that go together.

_____

_____

_____

_____

_____

_____

Notes for teachers

Help the children to read the target and to read the instructions: these are quite complicated and the children may need to read them several times. When you are confident that the children understand the activity, ask them to copy the sentences correctly. Can they match the questions and the answers? Do they remember to use question marks for the question sentences, full stops for the answer sentences, and capital letters for the starts of sentences and of people's names?

Target 7

> **Remember to use a capital letter at the start of each person's name. Remember to use question marks for questions.**

Sentence bank

who is the fastest runner in the class

the person with the best balance is lily

who is the best swimmer in the class

the fastest runner is callum

which person in the class can balance on one leg for longest

the best swimmer is kyle

Read the sentences in the sentence bank. Some of the sentences are questions. Some of the sentences are answers to the questions. Write the pairs of sentences that go together. Make sure that you use the correct punctuation.

_____

_____

_____

_____

_____

_____

Notes for teachers
Help the children to read the target and to read the instructions: these are quite complicated and the children may need to read them several times. When you are confident that the children understand the activity, ask them to copy the sentences correctly. Can they match the questions and the answers? Do they remember to use question marks for the question sentences, full stops for the answer sentences, and capital letters for the starts of sentences and of people's names?

Target 7

Remember to use a capital letter at the start of each person's name. Remember to use question marks for questions.

Sentence bank

kyle went to spain on holiday last year

who watched football with tom

at the weekend, mrs jones took jasmin to the zoo

tom and mr andrews watched a football match

where did jasmin go at the weekend

which country did kyle visit last year

Read the sentences in the sentence bank. Some of the sentences are questions. Some of the sentences are answers to the questions. Write the pairs of sentences that go together. Make sure that you use the correct punctuation.

_____

_____

_____

_____

_____

_____

Notes for teachers
Ask the children to read the target and to read the instructions. When you are confident that the children understand the activity, ask them to copy the sentences correctly. Can they match the questions and the answers? Do they remember to use question marks for the question sentences, full stops for the answer sentences, and capital letters for the starts of sentences and of people's names?

Remember to use a capital letter for the start of each day of the week. Remember to use question marks for questions.

Target 8

Remember to use a capital letter for the start of each day of the week.

Remember to use question marks for questions.

Word bank

Monday   Tuesday   Wednesday   Thursday   Friday
Saturday   Sunday

Copy each question sentence. Write a reply for each question.

What did you do on Saturday?

_____

_____

_____

What day was it yesterday?

_____

_____

_____

What day will it be tomorrow?

_____

_____

_____

Notes for teachers
Help the children to read the target and to read the instructions. When you are confident that the children understand the activity, ask them to copy the question sentences correctly. Can they think of suitable answers? Do they remember to use question marks for the question sentences, full stops for the answer sentences, and capital letters for the starts of sentences and of the names of the days?

Target 8

Remember to use a capital letter for the start of each day of the week.

Remember to use question marks for questions.

The question sentences below are not written correctly. Write each question sentence using the correct punctuation. Write a reply for each question.

Word bank
Monday   Tuesday
Wednesday   Thursday
Friday   Saturday   Sunday

did you do anything special on saturday or sunday

_____

_____

_____

on what day do you go swimming

_____

_____

_____

Write your own question about a day of the week.

_____

_____

Write an answer to the question.

_____

_____

Notes for teachers
Help the children to read the target and the instructions. When you are confident that the children understand the activity, ask them to copy the question sentences correctly. Can they think of suitable answers? Do they remember to use question marks for the question sentences, full stops for the answer sentences, and capital letters for the starts of sentences and of the names of the days?

Target 8

Remember to use a capital letter for the start of each day of the week.
Remember to use question marks for questions.

The question sentences below are not written correctly. Write each question sentence using the correct punctuation. Write a reply for each question.

where did you go on saturday

_____

_____

_____

do you attend any clubs during the week

_____

_____

_____

Write your own question about a day of the week.

_____

_____

Write an answer to the question.

_____

_____

Notes for teachers
Ask the children to read the target and the instructions. Do they remember to use question marks for the question sentences, full stops for the answer sentences, and capital letters for the starts of sentences and of the names of the days? As an extension activity you could ask the pupils to write a question for every day of the week.

Remember to use a capital letter for the start of each month of the year. Remember to use question marks for questions.

Remember to use a capital letter for the start of each month of the year.
Remember to use question marks for questions.

Word bank
January   February   March   April   May   June   July
August   September   October   November   December

Copy each question sentence. Write a reply for each question.

What is the first month of the year?

_____

_____

What is the sixth month of the year?

_____

_____

What is the twelfth month of the year?

_____

_____

Write your own question about a month of the year.

_____

_____

Notes for teachers
Help the children to read the target and to read the instructions. When you are confident that the children understand the activity, ask them to copy the question sentences correctly. Can they think of suitable answers? Do they remember to use question marks for the question sentences, full stops for the answer sentences, and capital letters for the starts of sentences and of the names of the months?

Target 9

Remember to use a capital letter for the start of each month of the year.
Remember to use question marks for questions.

The question sentences below are not written correctly. Write each question sentence using the correct punctuation. Write a reply for each question.

in what season is the month of july

_____
_____
_____

can you name two of the winter months

_____
_____
_____

Write your own question about a month of the year.

_____
_____

Write an answer to the question.

_____
_____

Notes for teachers
When you are confident that the children understand the activity, ask them to copy the question sentences correctly. Can they think of suitable answers? Do they remember to use question marks for the question sentences, full stops for the answer sentences, and capital letters for the starts of sentences and of the names of the months?

Target 9

Remember to use a capital letter for the start of each month of the year.
Remember to use question marks for questions.

The question sentences below are not written correctly. Write each question sentence using the correct punctuation. Write a reply for each question.

which month comes before july and which month comes after july

_____

_____

_____

which is the shortest month of the year how many days does it have normally

_____

_____

_____

Write your own question about a month of the year.

_____

_____

Write an answer to the question.

_____

_____

Notes for teachers
Ask the children to read the target and the instructions. Do they notice that the second exercise consists of two sentences both of which should end with a question mark? Can they compose appropriate answers to the questions? Do they remember to use question marks for the question sentences, full stops for the answer sentences, and capital letters for the starts of sentences and of the names of the months?

Remember when to write commas in lists.

Remember when to write commas in lists.

Kyle, Jas and Liz are helping Mum in the supermarket. They each have a list of things to buy.

Copy this sentence:

Kyle has to buy milk, bread and butter.

_____

Write a sentence about what Jas has to buy.

_____

_____

Write a sentence about what Liz has to buy.

_____

_____

Notes for teachers

Encourage the children to read the target and the other information provided. Point out that each child has three items on the shopping list but that when the list is contained in a sentence only one comma is needed: the three items are separated by one comma and the word 'and'. The activity could be extended by asking the children to make their own lists of items to buy.

Target 10

Remember when to write commas in lists.

Kyle, Jas and Liz are helping Mum in the supermarket. They each have a list of things to buy.

potatoes
onions
carrots
parsnips

raspberries
strawberries
cherries
peaches

leeks
beans
tomatoes
lettuce

Copy this sentence:

Kyle has to buy potatoes, onions, carrots and parsnips.

_____

Write a sentence about what Jas has to buy.

_____

_____

Write a sentence about what Liz has to buy.

_____

_____

Notes for teachers
Encourage the children to read the target and the other information provided. Point out that each child has four items on the shopping list but that when the list is contained in a sentence only two commas needed: the four items are separated by using two commas and the word 'and'. The activity could be extended by asking the children to make their own lists of items to buy.

Target 10

Remember when to write commas in lists.

Kyle, Jas and Liz are helping Mum in the supermarket. They each have a list of things to buy.

Copy this sentence:

Kyle has to buy Corn Flakes, Bran Flakes, Weetos and Rice Pops.

_____

_____

_____

Write a sentence about what Jas has to buy.

_____

_____

Write a sentence about what Liz has to buy.

_____

_____

Notes for teachers

Encourage the children to read the target and the other information provided. Point out that each child has four items on the shopping list but that when the list is contained in a sentence only two commas needed: the four items are separated by using two commas and the word 'and'. Talk about the fact that some of the items have capital initial letters because they are trade names. The activity could be extended by asking the children to make their own lists of items to buy.

Remember when to write commas in lists. Remember to use question marks for questions.

Remember when to write commas in lists.
Remember to use question marks for questions.

Copy each question. Write an answer sentence for each question.

Would you like to do maths, literacy or art next?

_____

_____

_____

_____

Do you like apples, oranges or bananas best?

_____

_____

_____

_____

Would you like fish, chips and beans for tea?

_____

_____

_____

_____

Notes for teachers
Encourage the children to read the target and the instructions. Point out that each sentence is a question and contains a list of three items, which are separated by one comma and the word 'or' or 'and'. Do they write an appropriate sentence as an answer for each question? As an extension activity, you could ask the children to write their own question sentence containing a list of items.

Target 11

Remember when to write commas in lists.
Remember to use question marks for questions.

Copy each question. Write an answer sentence for each question.

Where are my coat, scarf and gloves?

_____

_____

_____

Would you like to play hide-and-seek, rounders, tennis or football?

_____

_____

_____

Write two question sentences that each includes a list of items.
Remember to use commas where you need them.

_____

_____

_____

_____

Notes for teachers
Encourage the children to read the target and the instructions. Point out that each sentence is a question and contains a list of three or four items, which are separated by either one or two commas and the word 'or' or 'and'. Do they write an appropriate sentence as an answer for each question? The pupils may need help with ideas for their own two questions.

Target 11

Remember when to write commas in lists.
Remember to use question marks for questions.

Copy each question. Write an answer sentence for each question.

Have you got any pencil crayons, felt pens, paints or wax crayons?

_____

_____

_____

Would you like to go swimming, play football or watch television?

_____

_____

_____

Write two question sentences that each includes a list of items.
Remember to use commas where you need them.

_____

_____

_____

_____

Notes for teachers
Encourage the children to read the target and the instructions. Point out that each sentence is a question and contains a list of three or four items, which are separated by either one or two commas and the word 'or'. Discuss the second sentence, explaining that each item consists of a phrase, ie 'go swimming', 'play football' and 'watch television'. The pupils may need help with ideas for their own two questions.

Remember to use inverted commas for speech.

Copy the conversation below.

"My name is Jasmin," said the girl.

"My name is Tom," said the boy.

_____

_____

"I am eight years old," said Jasmin.

"I am seven years old," said Tom.

_____

_____

Notes for teachers

Discuss the page carefully with the children. Explain that the inverted commas (speech marks) are used to show the actual words spoken. The opening speech marks curve inwards and are placed before the words spoken; the closing speech marks curve inwards and are placed after the comma that follows the words spoken. Note that the sentence ends after 'said the girl' or 'said the boy'. You may wish to extend the activity by dictating some short speech sentences such as: "Hello," said the girl. "How are you?" asked the boy.

Target 12

Copy the conversation below.

"How old are you?" asked the girl.

"I am seven years old," said the boy.

_____

_____

"I am older than you," said the girl.

"I am younger than you," said the boy.

_____

_____

Notes for teachers
Discuss the page carefully with the children. Explain that the inverted commas (speech marks) are used to show the actual words spoken. The opening speech marks curve inwards and are placed before the words spoken; the closing speech marks curve inwards and are placed after the question mark or comma that follows the words spoken. Note that the sentence ends after 'asked the girl' or 'said the boy'. You may wish to extend the activity by dictating some short speech sentences such as: "I like football," said the girl. "Where do you play?" asked the boy.

Target 12

Remember to use inverted commas for speech.

Copy the conversation below.

"What day is it today?" asked the girl.

"I think it is Thursday," said the boy.

_____

_____

"It might be Tuesday," said the girl.

"But it could be Friday," said the boy.

_____

_____

Notes for teachers
Discuss the page carefully with the children. Explain that the inverted commas (speech marks) are used to show the actual words spoken. The opening speech marks curve inwards and are placed before the words spoken; the closing speech marks curve inwards and are placed after the question mark or comma that follows the words spoken. Note that the sentence ends after 'asked the girl' or 'said the boy'. You may wish to extend the activity by dictating some short speech sentences such as: "I like the weekend," said the girl. "I prefer school days," said the boy.

Remember to use inverted commas for speech. Remember to use question marks for questions.

Remember to use inverted commas for speech. Remember to use question marks for questions.

Copy the conversation below.

"What is your name?" asked Joe.

"My name is Sam," replied Sam.

_____

_____

"How old are you?" asked Joe.

"I am eight years old," replied Sam.

_____

_____

"What year are you in?" asked Joe.

"I am in Year 3," replied Sam.

_____

_____

Notes for teachers

Discuss the page carefully with the children. Remind them that the inverted commas (speech marks) are used to show the actual words spoken. The opening speech marks curve inwards and are placed before the words spoken; the closing speech marks curve inwards and are placed after the question mark or comma that follows the words spoken. Point out the use of the words 'asked' and 'replied'. You could extend the activity by asking the children to compose their own question sentences: a pair of children could ask each other questions orally, then attempt to write out part of their conversation.

Target 13

**Remember to use inverted commas for speech.
Remember to use question marks for questions.**

Copy the conversation below.

"When is your birthday?" asked Jenny.

"My birthday is in January," replied Scott.

_____

_____

"How old will you be on your next birthday?" asked Jenny.

"I will be nine next year," replied Scott.

_____

_____

"Will you have a birthday party?" asked Jenny.

"I might do," replied Scott.

_____

_____

Notes for teachers

Discuss the page carefully with the children. Remind them that the inverted commas (speech marks) are used to show the actual words spoken. The opening speech marks curve inwards and are placed before the words spoken; the closing speech marks curve inwards and are placed after the question mark or comma that follows the words spoken. Point out the use of the words 'asked' and 'replied'. You could extend the activity by asking the children to continue the conversation between Jenny and Scott.

Target 13

> **Remember to use inverted commas for speech.**
> **Remember to use question marks for questions.**

Copy the conversation below.

"What is your favourite subject at school?" asked Mum.

"I think I like maths best," I replied.

_____

_____

"How often do you do maths?" asked Mum.

"We do it every day except Wednesday," I replied.

_____

_____

"Why not on Wednesday?" asked Mum.

"Because we go swimming every Wednesday," I explained.

_____

_____

Notes for teachers
Discuss the page carefully with the children. Remind them that the inverted commas (speech marks) are used to show the actual words spoken. The opening speech marks curve inwards and are placed before the words spoken; the closing speech marks curve inwards and are placed after the question mark or comma that follows the words spoken. Point out the use of the words 'asked' and 'replied'. You could extend the activity by asking the children to continue the conversation between the mother and the child. You may wish to point out that 'Mum' has a capital letter because it is a name but that 'my mum' would not have a capital letter.

Remember to use inverted commas for speech. Remember to use exclamation marks to express strong feelings.

Remember to use inverted commas for speech.
Remember to use exclamation marks to express strong feelings.

Copy the sentences below.

"Come here right now!"
called the owner of the dog.

_____

_____

_____

"I love Fridays!" said Mum.

_____

"I am very angry!" said the teacher.

_____

"That baby is so cute!" said the girl.

_____

Notes for teachers
Discuss the page carefully with the children. Remind them that the inverted commas (speech marks) are used to show the actual words spoken. The opening speech marks curve inwards and are placed before the words spoken; the closing speech marks curve inwards and are placed after the exclamation mark that follows the words spoken. Point out that each sentence has an exclamation mark after the words spoken as strong feelings are being expressed.

Target 14

> **Remember to use inverted commas for speech.**
> **Remember to use exclamation marks to express strong feelings.**

Copy the sentences below.

"You two are always arguing!"
said Mum crossly.

_____

_____

_____

"It is a lovely day today!" said the teacher.

_____

"I love chocolate!" said Katie.

_____

"That is a lovely car!" exclaimed the man.

_____

Notes for teachers
Discuss the page carefully with the children. Remind them that the inverted commas (speech marks) are used to show the actual words spoken. The opening speech marks curve inwards and are placed before the words spoken; the closing speech marks curve inwards and are placed after the exclamation mark that follows the words spoken. Point out that each sentence has an exclamation mark after the words spoken as strong feelings are being expressed. Note the use of the word 'exclaimed', again showing strong feelings.

Target 14

Remember to use inverted commas for speech.
Remember to use exclamation marks to express strong feelings.

Copy the sentences below.

"Get out of my sight!" said the teacher to the naughty boy.

_____

_____

_____

"What fantastic work!" exclaimed the teacher, looking at the art work on the wall.

_____

_____

"Give me back my sweets!" demanded the toddler.

_____

"Watch out!" shouted the woodcutter as the tree began to fall.

_____

Notes for teachers
Discuss the page carefully with the children. Remind them that the inverted commas (speech marks) are used to show the actual words spoken. The opening speech marks curve inwards and are placed before the words spoken; the closing speech marks curve inwards and are placed after the exclamation mark that follows the words spoken. Point out that each sentence has an exclamation mark after the words spoken as strong feelings are being expressed. Can the children think of their own exclamations and write them out with appropriate punctuation?

Remember to use inverted commas for speech within conversations.

Remember to use inverted commas for speech within conversations.

Here is a conversation between two people.

"What are you doing on Saturday?" asked Jasdeep.

"I am going shopping with my mum," replied Nell.

"How about Sunday then?" asked Jasdeep.

"We are going to the seaside," replied Nell.

What do you think they said next? Write some more of their conversation.

_____

_____

_____

_____

_____

Notes for teachers

Read through the conversation carefully with the children. Point out the features of a written conversation:

1 Speech marks (inverted commas) are used at each end of the spoken words;

2 The closing speech marks are never alone – there is always a comma, a question mark, an exclamation mark or a full stop **before** the closing speech marks;

3 A new line is started every time the speaker changes.

Together with all these rules, the children still have to remember to use capital letters appropriately and to end each sentence with a full stop! (Or even an exclamation mark!)

Target 15

Remember to use inverted commas for speech within conversations.

Here is a conversation between two people.

"Do you want to play football tomorrow?" asked Tariq.

"No, I have to go to swimming practice," replied Jez.

"How about after you go swimming?" asked Tariq.

"No, my mum is making me tidy my room!" said Jez crossly.

What do you think they said next? Write some more of their conversation.

_____

_____

_____

_____

_____

_____

Notes for teachers

Read through the conversation carefully with the children. Point out the features of a written conversation:

1 Speech marks (inverted commas) are used at each end of the spoken words;

2 The closing speech marks are never alone – there is always a comma, a question mark, an exclamation mark or a full stop **before** the closing speech marks;

3 A new line is started every time the speaker changes.

Together with all these rules, the children still have to remember to use capital letters appropriately and to end each sentence with a full stop! (Or even an exclamation mark!)

Target 15

Remember to use inverted commas for speech within conversations.

Here is a conversation between two people.

"My class have worked very hard this morning so we are going to play all afternoon," said Mrs Brown.
"My class have worked hard this morning and they are going to work hard this afternoon!" responded Mrs Strauss sharply.
"They need to have some fun sometimes," said Mrs Brown.
"We are not here for fun!" snapped Mrs Strauss.

Write a short conversation between two people. They could be children, adults or one child and one adult.

_____

_____

_____

_____

_____

_____

_____

_____

Notes for teachers

Read through the conversation carefully with the children. Point out the features of a written conversation:

1 Speech marks (inverted commas) are used at each end of the spoken words;
2 The closing speech marks are never alone – there is always a comma, a question mark, an exclamation mark or a full stop **before** the closing speech marks;
3 A new line is started every time the speaker changes.

Together with all these rules, the children still have to remember to use capital letters appropriately and to end each sentence with a full stop! (Or even an exclamation mark!)